William Tell
of Switzerland

A Tale for Tiny Travellers, adapted by Liz Tay
Illustrated by Rubén Carral Fajardo

www.talesfortinytravellers.com

Once upon a time, hundreds of years ago, Switzerland was ruled by an old, powerful family called the Habsburgs.

The Habsburgs had plenty of land and money, but they were cruel and selfish.

4

They liked to control the people who lived
in their lands, and made them do
silly things like bow down to a hat.

High in the mountains of Uri, a hunter named William Tell was sick of the Habsburgs and their tyranny.

He thought that bowing down
to a hat was simply ridiculous.

ALTDORF

So he didn't.

When the town's governor saw what William Tell had done, he wanted to punish and frighten him.

He tied William Tell's son
up against a tree and refused to
let him go unless William Tell could shoot
an apple off the top of the boy's head.

11

William Tell was an expert marksman. Even so, he worried that he might miss the apple and hurt his son.

WHOOSH!

His bolt flew straight through the air, splitting the apple neatly in two!

Quick as a flash, William Tell
loaded a second bolt
into his crossbow.

He planned to end the governor's cruelty once and for all.

News of William Tell's bravery spread across the land.

Soon, people from all over Switzerland realised that they'd had enough of being bullied, too.

19

Rebels met in secret and promised to fight together for freedom from the Habsburgs.

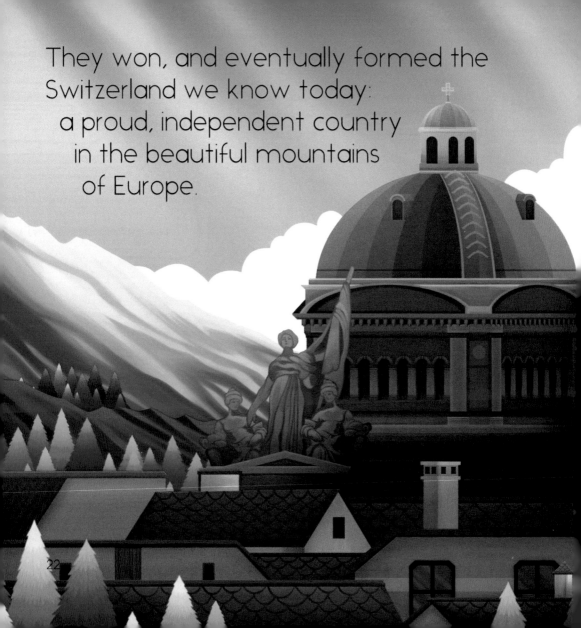

They won, and eventually formed the
Switzerland we know today:
  a proud, independent country
  in the beautiful mountains
  of Europe.

Notes for Tiny Travellers

Much of the land we now know as Switzerland was once controlled by the Habsburg family, which originated in northern Switzerland, where their 11th century fortress, the Habsburg Castle (page 3), still stands.

Some regions were also controlled by German, French and Italian nobles. Modern-day Switzerland thus has four official languages: German, French, Italian and Romansh.

While no one knows for sure if William Tell actually existed, his likeness features on Switzerland's 5 Franc coins, and there is a monument to him in the picturesque town of Altdorf, Central Switzerland, where the hat incident (page 9) is said to have taken place.

The Swiss Charter of Confederation (page 21) joined the Uri, Schwyz and Nidwalden regions in 1291 and formed the basis of today's Switzerland. The alliance was supposedly struck in the Rütli Meadow (page 21), which overlooks Lake Lucerne.

The Charter document is now housed in the Museum of the Swiss Charters (Bundesbriefmuseum) in Schwyz.

This is an abridged version of the William Tell legend. In other versions, William Tell is sentenced to life in prison after successfully shooting the apple, but escapes en route to the dungeon at Küssnacht and assassinates the tyrannical governor instead.

A Catholic chapel called Tellskapelle stands on the shore of Lake Lucerne to mark the spot of William Tell's legendary escape, while a small pavilion at Hohle Gasse marks the narrow lane where the assassination is said to have occurred.

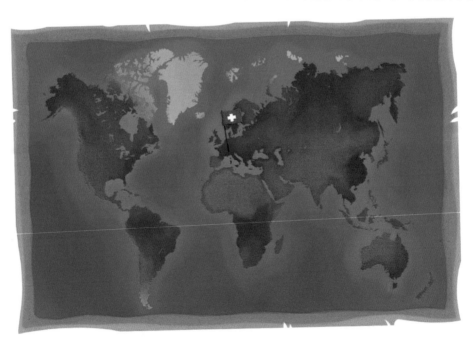

74121332R00015

Made in the USA
Columbia, SC
09 September 2019